JN071693

英単語検定
単検

公式問題集

1級

一般財団法人
日本英会話協会
監修

三恵社

英単語検定（単検）とは

　「英単語検定（単検）」は、（財）日本英会話協会による英単語に特化した資格検定試験です。2009年11月に第1回試験を開催して以来、小学生からご年配の方まで幅広く受験を頂いています。英語、英会話の習得で最も大切な『語彙力』に重点を置いた試験問題で、TOEIC®や英検のような複雑な文法、長文読解問題はありません。

　昨今の日本において、グローバル化の加速は増すばかりです。その証拠として、小学校、中学校、高等学校で外国人教師（英語圏出身）による授業の強化、必須化。また、英語を社内公用語にする企業の増大…。

　ではど、どうすれば効果的に英語力を向上させることができるか？
　大切なことは、一つでも多くの語彙、単語を習得することです。英語の長文読解は、英単語が分かれば（全体の）70％は理解できるといわれています。おそらく、単語の意味を理解することで（その）周辺の文章の内容が自然と類推できるからでしょう。

　本書は、『問題』と『解答』に分かれています。『問題』は過去に開催された試験に用いられた内容をそのまま掲載しており、1回分（100問）の解答に35分で取り組めば本番のテストの予行演習としてもご利用頂けます。『解答』には、『問題』の解答が表となってまとめられており、簡単に答え合わせができます。過去の問題を級ごとに分けて問題集を構成しているため、ご自身の学習レベルに合わせた学習はもとより、周辺の級にもチャレンジできるので本番の準備とご自身のレベルの確認を同時に行うことができます。

　英単語検定（単検）に関心を持たれている皆様が、本書により試験内容を十分に理解され、実際の受験に際して、実力を発揮されることを願っております。
　また、本書が英単語検定（単検）の受験に役立つ問題集として、お役に立つことを願っています。

（財）日本英会話協会

各級の問題形式

5 級	和訳 50 問	英訳 50 問		
4 級	和訳 45 問	英訳 45 問	英英(説明→単語) 5 問	英英(単語→説明) 5 問
3 級	和訳 45 問	英訳 45 問	英英(説明→単語) 5 問	英英(単語→説明) 5 問
準 2 級	和訳 40 問	英訳 40 問	英英(説明→単語) 10 問	英英(単語→説明) 10 問
2 級	和訳 40 問	英訳 40 問	英英(説明→単語) 10 問	英英(単語→説明) 10 問
準 1 級	和訳 35 問	英訳 35 問	英英(説明→単語) 15 問	英英(単語→説明) 15 問
1 級	和訳 35 問	英訳 35 問	英英(説明→単語) 15 問	英英(単語→説明) 15 問

※試験問題数は全級 100 問

試験概要

試験時間：35 分

試験方式：マークシート方式による、四者択一

実施頻度などの詳細情報については、ホームページ（www.eitangokentei.com）を
ご確認ください。

各級のレベルと必要語彙数

級	各級のレベルの目安	語彙数
5 級	中学生低学年レベル	約 400 語
4 級	中学生高学年レベル	約 800 語
3 級	中学校卒業レベル	約 1,200 語
準 2 級	高校低学年レベル	約 2,200 語
2 級	高校卒業レベル	約 2,600 語
準 1 級	大卒・社会人レベル	約 7,300 語
1 級	ネイティブレベル	約 12,000 語

推薦文

「私も、単検（英単語検定）をお薦めします。」

学習院中等科教諭：行名一夫先生

（単検 1 級保持者）

「単語力が重要であることは間違いないので、学習の動機
づけとして利用価値は高いと思います。単語でも、発音で
も、文法でも、会話でも、とにかく英語に興味を持って、
日々できることに取り組む、地道な努力を続けてください。
そのための手段として『単検』を応援します。」

団体受験校

小学校	聖心女子学院初等科	
中学校	学習院中等科 聖心女子学院中等科 海城中学校 十和田市立大深内中学校 札幌市立中島中学校 愛媛県西条北中学校 勝浦町立勝浦中学校 南三陸町立歌津中学校 大阪市立鶴橋中学校 小樽市立末広中学校 水戸市立千波中学校 木祖村立木祖中学校 鴻巣市立鴻巣南中学校 甲南中学校	南外中学校 豊郷町立豊日中学校 札幌市立中島中学校 登米市立南方中学校 中札内村立中札内中学校 筑波大学附属駒場中学校 湯田中学校 牛久市立牛久第三中学校 天草市立稜南中学校 大阪府守口市立梶中学校 小鹿野町立小鹿野中学校 五ヶ瀬中等教育学校 福岡市立席田中学校 朝倉市立南陵中学校
高校	明成高等学校 洛南高等学校 富岡西高等学校 修猷館高等学校 北海道共和高等学校 福岡県立春日高等学校 名古屋市立名東高等学校 三重県伊勢高等学校 岩手県種市高等学校 岡山県立笠岡高等学校 佐賀県立白石高等学校 沖縄カトリック高等学校 稲築志耕館高等学校 静岡県立伊東高等学校 旭川大学高等学校 金光藤蔭高等学校 小樽明峰高等学校	宮城県立米山高等学校 和歌山県立南部高等学校龍神分校 岡山県立高松農業高等学校 北海道大樹高等学校 松本第一高等学校 帯広北高等学校 高岡向陵高等学校 クラーク記念国際高等学校東京キャンパス クラーク記念国際高等学校姫路キャンパス クラーク記念国際高等学校厚木キャンパス クラーク記念国際高等学校鳥取キャンパス クラーク記念国際高等学校千葉キャンパス 一ツ葉高等学校福岡キャンパス 愛媛県立大洲農業高等学校 豊橋市立豊橋高等学校 人間環境大学岡崎学園高等学校 神戸村野工業高等学校
その他	東葛ゼミナール 房進学院	英会話ビギン

監修者紹介

◆チャールズ・カベル

アメリカ合衆国出身。アラバマ大学卒業。ペンシルバニア州立大学比較文学学部修士課程終了。ハーバード大学東アジア文明言語学科博士課程終了。

1987 年　文部省派遣による日立市市役所教育委員会英語指導助手。
2000 年～モンタナ大学現代及び古典言語・文学学部助教授。
2005 年～東洋大学文学部准教授。早稲田大学国際教養学部講師を併任。
イエール大学東アジア委員会博士会員。

アドバイザー紹介

◆川村　透

YEC 代表。企業の海外視察コーディネーター、英会話スクール講師を経て、2002 年に
YEC－ユア・イングリッシュ・コーチ代表に就任。翻訳家。

◆小林　好江

英国ウォーリック大学大学院英語教授法修士号。翻訳家。英会話講師。日本に住む
外国人にボランディアで生け花を指導。

◆加藤　いずみ

「英会話 Begin」代表。英語学習者向けサイト「みんなの英会話奮闘記」を運営。

◆吉澤　正之

LEO 代表。帰国生のための受験指導塾「LEO(Language Expert Organization)」
を運営。

日本英会話協会について

　（財）日本英会話協会は、2009 年に日本人の英会話力向上を目指し、世界で活躍する人材を育成するために設立されました。

●講演活動　●資格検定　●英会話に関する情報発信

　等で教育をサポートし、アジアで最下位と言われている日本人の英語力を上げ、世界で活躍できる人材と企業の育成に力を入れています。

◎「英会話検定」

　当協会で実施している、もう一つの検定をご紹介します。英会話レベルが判断できる程度の面接式試験を行い、当協会既定の必要な要素や基準で厳正な判定をしたうえで、受験者に 5 級～1 級の認定を与えます。

英会話検定の試験時間と合格レベル

級別	試験時間	合格レベル
ネイティブ A	20 分	時事的、文化的、思想的、哲学的な意見を豊かな表現力で述べることができる。ビジネス単語や、専門用語にも精通している。逆転的な発送をすることができ、思想の矛盾などを指摘することができる。
ネイティブ B		欧米で実際に使用されているイディオムを熟知している。時事問題などに関するディスカッションができ、倫理や道徳、思想に関する意見も述べることができる。
1 級	5～10 分	インタビュアーが出すトピックに関して詳しい、理にかなった説明と議論ができる。単語力も高く、表現力に優れる。読解能力も高い。
2 級		時事的な話の初歩段階でディスカッションできる。自分の意見をある程度表現する。
3 級		自分の趣味趣向に関して簡単な説明ができる。物事の説明や気持ちの表現が簡単にできる。
4 級		自己紹介ができる。簡単な英語の質問を理解し、正しい文法で応答ができる。
5 級		簡単な英語の質問を理解し、シンプルな英語で応答ができる。限られた語彙力の中でコミュニケーションをとることができる。

級の認定基準

　5～20分間のインタビューの中で、各級の認定を受けるためには全ての項目において、合格基準を満たす必要があります。各項目に5級～1級またはネイティブA・Bの判定を付けて、集計結果を基に級の認定を与えます。

　詳細はホームページ（http://www.eikaiwakentei.com/）をご覧ください。

級	基準項目
5～1級	1．Speaking：話す能力
	2．Listening：リスニング力
	3．Pronunciation：発音
	4．Vocabulary：語彙力
	5．Fluidity：流暢さ
	6．Grammar：文法
ネイティブ A・B	1．Pronunciation：発音
	2．Vocabulary：語彙力
	3．Fluidity：流暢さ
	4．Grammar：文法
	5．Listening：リスニング力／読解力
	6．Idioms：熟語
	7．Communication skills：コミュニケーションスキル
	8．Nuance accuracy：ニュアンスの正確性
	9．Ability to express opinions and feelings：感情や意見を述べる力
	10．Explaining skills：説明能力

目次

■英単語検定（単検）とは･････3

■各級の問題形式･････4

■試験概要･････4

■各級のレベルと必要語彙数･････5

■団体受験校･････6

■監修者・アドバイザー紹介･････7

■日本英会話協会について･････8

■問題

問題1･････11

問題1の解答･････30

問題2･････31

問題2の解答･････50

問題3･････51

問題3の解答･････70

問題4･････71

問題4の解答･････90

1級

問題①

① 次の1.から35.までの英単語の和訳として最も適切なものを1,2,3,4の中から一つ選びなさい。

1. erratic
1. とっぴな　　2. 驚くべき　　3. 誤った　　4. わかりにくい

2. emissary
1. スパイ　　2. 外交員　　3. 少佐　　4. 大臣

3. hiatus
1. 連続　　2. すき間　　3. 境目　　4. 両脇

4. tenancy
1. 地質　　2. 大地　　3. 地形　　4. 借地

5. sever
1. 割り込む　　2. 切り離す　　3. 取り押さえる　　4. 巻きつける

6. hearten
1. 励ます　　2. 愛する　　3. 生き返らす　　4. 心折れる

7. negate
1. 否定する　　2. 交渉する　　3. 取り交わす　　4. 混乱する

8.　extemporaneous
1. 超越した　　2. 即席の　　3. 強力な　　4. 優れた

9.　trough
1. 台風の目　　2. 季節の変わり目　　3. 気圧の谷　　4. 気温の急変

10.　confluence
1. 作品　　2. 補助　　3. 欲求　　4. 合流

11.　murky
1. においのきつい　　2. 後ろめたい　　3. 特筆すべき　　4. 脂の乗った

12.　chronology
1. 年表　　2. 成仏　　3. 減額　　4. 禁句

13.　creak
1. 割れ目　　2. きしみ　　3. 欠けら　　4. にごり

14.　rejoinder
1. 出戻り　　2. 反抗　　3. 再選　　4. 応答

15. vicinity
1. 奴隷　2. 圧勝　3. 近所　4. 反乱

16. ruminate
1. 熟考する　2. 思い出す　3. 逸脱する　4. 手伝う

17. stagnant
1. 精密な　2. 停滞した　3. 活発な　4. 重宝な

18. giddy
1. 足取りの軽い　2. 派手な　3. めまいがする　4. 浮ついた

19. incinerator
1. 焼却炉　2. 屋根裏　3. 特設会場　4. 集積場

20. chum
1. 親友　2. 恋人　3. 味方　4. 敵

21. tenement
1. 偽証　2. 借家　3. えん罪　4. 調教師

22. microbe
1. 病原菌　　2. 顕微鏡　　3. 検査薬　　4. 最小単位

23. grudge
1. 焦がす　　2. 煎る　　3. 使い果たす　　4. 出し惜しむ

24. cub
1. 獣医　　2. 珍獣　　3. 怪獣　　4. 幼獣

25. coddle
1. 充満する　　2. 諭す　　3. 緊迫する　　4. 甘やかす

26. reprieve
1. 証人尋問　　2. 弁論　　3. 上告　　4. 執行猶予

27. repatriate
1. 本国へ送還する　　2. 自国を愛する　　3. 領土を奪う　　4. 食料を配る

28. subversion
1. 代替案　　2. 転覆　　3. 予告編　　4. 変更点

29.　gullible

1. 取りやすい　　2. 酔いやすい　　3. だまされやすい　　4. 付き合いやすい

30.　constrict

1. 構成する　　2. 付け加える　　3. 締めつける　　4. 建てる

31.　strenuous

1. 強靭な　　2. 精力的な　　3. 心配性な　　4. 保全的な

32.　contravene

1. 反省する　　2. 飛躍する　　3. 違反する　　4. 馬鹿にする

33.　jumble

1. 破産する　　2. 取り除く　　3. ごちゃまぜにする　　4. 屈んで進む

34.　prowl

1. ひったくる　　2. まとわりつく　　3. ひるむ　　4. うろつく

35.　rebuttal

1. 再戦　　2. 反感　　3. 成果　　4. 反証

36. 委託販売
1. containment　2. contraception　3. conundrum　4. consignment

37. 締め出す
1. fortify　2. forgo　3. forestall　4. foreclose

38. 綿密に調べる
1. insinuate　2. scrutinize　3. unearth　4. substantiate

39. 無気力な
1. caustic　2. haggard　3. lethargic　4. perennial

40. 偽造の
1. intravenous　2. counterfeit　3. privy　4. illicit

41. 簡潔な
1. terse　2. dour　3. morose　4. pensive

42. かじかんだ
1. burly　2. timidity　3. baggy　4. numb

43. 軌道
1. funnel　　2. environs　　3. zodiac　　4. trajectory

44. 降水
1. precipitation　　2. knack　　3. propensity　　4. pollen

45. 不活性な
1. invalidate　　2. unorthodox　　3. incumbent　　4. inert

46. むさ苦しい
1. crafty　　2. canny　　3. sanguine　　4. squalid

47. 大火災
1. conflagration　　2. precipice　　3. eviction　　4. combustion

48. 浪費する
1. squander　　2. exult　　3. deviate　　4. exacerbate

49. 報復
1. excise　　2. probation　　3. vengeance　　4. decadence

50. わめく
1. relegate　　2. engulf　　3. defamation　　4. rant

51. 名誉毀損
1. cessation　　2. libel　　3. wreckage　　4. recourse

52. なぞ
1. incursion　　2. enigma　　3. graphite　　4. repository

53. かま
1. sickle　　2. furrow　　3. aria　　4. baloney

54. つむじ風
1. whirlwind　　2. epilepsy　　3. fortress　　4. wicker

55. 倹約な
1. stocky　　2. thrifty　　3. prodigious　　4. pompous

56. 侵略する
1. encroach　　2. astound　　3. enshrine　　4. daunt

57. おとなしい
1. covert　　2. demure　　3. indolent　　4. austere

58. 秘義の
1. sardonic　　2. dainty　　3. auxiliary　　4. esoteric

59. はつらつとした
1. paramount　　2. effervescent　　3. imminent　　4. adamant

60. 挿入語句
1. ellipse　　2. terminology　　3. puncture　　4. parenthesis

61. ずるい
1. intractable　　2. politic　　3. semantic　　4. flippant

62. 分離した
1. translucent　　2. tempestuous　　3. utilitarian　　4. discrete

63. 調和しない
1. incongruous　　2. ominous　　3. inadvertent　　4. unscrupulous

64. いんちきの
1. exorbitant   2. nondescript   3. oblivious   4. bogus

65. 船尾に
1. ablaze   2. aft   3. impromptu   4. asunder

66. 不細工
1. bastion   2. malaise   3. hefty   4. botch

67. 気難しい
1. tenuous   2. peevish   3. neural   4. precocious

68. けいれん
1. convulsion   2. asthma   3. fluff   4. tantrum

69. 隔離する
1. exude   2. sequester   3. vouch   4. romp

70. 見かけ倒しの
1. vociferous   2. shoddy   3. insipid   4. inexorable

③ 次の71. から85. までの説明文に最も適切な単語を、1,2,3,4の中から一つ
選びなさい。

71. to make an organization or system less effective or powerful
1. stagnate　　2. debilitate　　3. despondent　　4. smolder

72. talking continuously in an excited or anxious way
1. lenient　　2. taut　　3. delirious　　4. hale

73. to be the cause of a situation or feeling
1. reimburse　　2. resumption　　3. flaunt　　4. engender

74. determined to do something and unwilling to stop trying
1. tenacious　　2. sensual　　3. lax　　4. benign

75. to make someone feel calm or as if they want to sleep
1. arousal　　2. lull　　3. tangle　　4. tarnish

76. to criticize someone in a way that shows you do not think they are good
1. deplete　　2. disparage　　3. deprave　　4. depose

77. small pieces of colored paper that you throw into the air over people

1. placebo   2. confetti   3. dune   4. jettison

78. to become more cheerful and interested in what is happening around you

1. propagate   2. consummate   3. supersede   4. perk

79. a strong feeling of not liking somebody or something

1. slander   2. treason   3. retribution   4. aversion

80. to make something more beautiful by adding decorations to it

1. rejuvenate   2. embellish   3. construe   4. galvanize

81. a situation in which one state or country controls others

1. avarice   2. hegemony   3. merriment   4. insurrection

82. working or staying somewhere for only a short time

1. transient   2. cursory   3. derelict   4. visionary

83. a tall pointed structure on the top of a building, especially a church

1. spire　　2. gland　　3. usher　　4. crypt

84. involving all the members of a committee or organization

1. confederate　　2. futility　　3. plenary　　4. pertinent

85. to completely destroy a building or town so that nothing is left

1. stipulate　　2. coalesce　　3. raze　　4. succumb

④ 次の86.から100.までの単語に最も適切な説明文を、1,2,3,4の中から一
　つ選びなさい。

86. tactical

1. openly refusing to obey somebody or something, sometimes in an aggressive way
2. helping you to deal with a problem quickly and effectively
3. connected with the particular method you use to achieve something
4. according to a scientific idea that has not been proven to be true in a practical way

87. waft

1. to move or make something move gently through the air
2. to stand, sit or move in a lazy way often with your shoulders and head bent forward
3. to take, carry or transport somebody or something from one place to another
4. to become or to make something larger, wider or more open

88. blight

1. to spoil or damage something especially by causing a lot of problems
2. to aim or point the light of a lamp in a particular direction
3. to make something such as a law or a political or religious system less strict
4. to start burning or to make something start burning

89. scurry

1. to move quickly with short steps, especially because you are in a hurry
2. to walk with an effort through something, especially water or mud
3. to walk proudly swinging your shoulders in a way that shows you are very confident
4. to make quick and light sounds as a surface is being hit several times

90. sagacious

1. very expensive and looking very impressive
2. able to understand and judge things very well
3. consisting of many different kinds of things that are not connected
4. able to do things and make decisions without help from anyone else

91. bigotry

1. the condition of being dirty and unpleasant because of a lack of care or money
2. the state of feeling or the act of expressing strong and unreasonable beliefs or opinions
3. the quality of thinking or behaving in a correct and honest way
4. the belief that something good will not happen or that something is not important

92. fraternity

1. a group of people sharing the same profession, interests or beliefs
2. an arrangement to meet somebody at a particular time and place
3. a journey to a place connected with someone or something famous
4. a thing or a person that is used to trick somebody into doing what you want them to do

93. disseminate

1. to make someone breathe again or become conscious after they have almost died
2. to spread information or ideas to as many people as possible
3. to make somebody or something seem less important or successful
4. to offer so much of a product for sale that there is more than people want to buy

94. arthritis

1. a very serious disease in which cells in one part of the body start to grow
2. a disease that causes the joints of your body to become swollen and very painful
3. the condition of being larger or rounder than normal
4. a crack or broken part in a bone or other hard substance

95. devious

1. having two halves, parts or sides that are the same in size and shape
2. to be extremely interested in something
3. behaving in a dishonest or indirect way or tricking people in order to get something
4. unwilling to stop opposing somebody or something

96. fluffy

1. looking as if it is soft and light
2. lying on the ground and facing downwards
3. changing often and suddenly
4. happening or appearing several times

97. mundane

1. concerned with ordinary daily life rather than religious matters
2. following closely the traditional beliefs and practices of a religion
3. behaving calmly and not seeming interested in anything or worried about anything
4. showing signs that something is likely to be successful in the future

98.　scruple

1. a sudden feeling that you would like to do or have something
2. an amount of money that is given to someone as a reward for doing something
3. a feeling that prevents you from doing something that you think may be morally wrong
4. a lively and enjoyable activity during which people forget their responsibilities

99.　soot

1. a machine for making cloth by twisting threads between other threads
2. black powder that is produced when wood or coal is burnt
3. a substance used for cleaning surfaces or for making them smooth
4. a wild or garden plant, with a large delicate flower that is usually red

100.　interminable

1. not moving but ready to move or do something at any moment
2. lasting a very long time and therefore boring or annoying
3. having spiritual powers or qualities that are difficult to understand or to explain
4. not having to explain or give reasons for your actions to anyone

解答

問1	問2	問3	問4	問5	問6	問7	問8	問9	問10
1	1	2	4	2	1	1	2	3	4
問11	問12	問13	問14	問15	問16	問17	問18	問19	問20
2	1	2	4	3	1	2	3	1	1
問21	問22	問23	問24	問25	問26	問27	問28	問29	問30
2	1	4	4	4	4	1	2	3	3
問31	問32	問33	問34	問35	問36	問37	問38	問39	問40
2	3	3	4	4	4	4	2	3	2
問41	問42	問43	問44	問45	問46	問47	問48	問49	問50
1	4	4	1	4	4	1	1	3	4
問51	問52	問53	問54	問55	問56	問57	問58	問59	問60
2	2	1	1	2	1	2	4	2	4
問61	問62	問63	問64	問65	問66	問67	問68	問69	問70
2	4	1	4	2	4	2	1	2	2
問71	問72	問73	問74	問75	問76	問77	問78	問79	問80
2	3	4	1	2	2	2	4	4	2
問81	問82	問83	問84	問85	問86	問87	問88	問89	問90
2	1	1	3	3	3	1	1	1	2
問91	問92	問93	問94	問95	問96	問97	問98	問99	問100
2	1	2	2	3	1	1	3	2	2

1級

問題②

① 次の1. から35. までの英単語の和訳として最も適切なものを1,2,3,4の中から一つ選びなさい。

1. tenet
1. 奥儀　　2. 主義　　3. 流儀　　4. 審議

2. moribund
1. まだらの　　2. 無数の　　3. 夜行性の　　4. ひん死の

3. livestock
1. 非常食　　2. 家畜　　3. 人気株　　4. 脂肪

4. qualm
1. 束縛　　2. 気取り　　3. 吐き気　　4. 海底

5. debilitate
1. 減少させる　　2. ぞっとさせる　　3. 長引かせる　　4. 衰弱させる

6. deplore
1. 不運をもたらす　　2. 隠ぺいする　　3. 遺憾に思う　　4. 無効にする

7. nibble
1. 隠し持つ　　2. 揺り動かす　　3. 少しずつかじる　　4. 包む

8.　elude
1. ねじ曲げる　　2. 可能にする　　3. 逃れる　　4. 取り消す

9.　detention
1. 降格　　2. 弁解　　3. 違反　　4. 拘留

10.　node
1. 要塞　　2. 濃霧　　3. 祝福　　4. こぶ

11.　ferocious
1. 優秀な　　2. 凶暴な　　3. 平凡な　　4. 難解な

12.　dislodge
1. 裏切る　　2. 解錠する　　3. 加担する　　4. 除去する

13.　buff
1. 磨く　　2. 免れる　　3. 覆す　　4. せがむ

14.　supersede
1. 絶賛する　　2. 取って代わる　　3. 競り勝つ　　4. よみがえらせる

15. wheeze
1. ぜいぜい息する　　2. ずるずる吸う　　3. ぐいぐい飲む　　4. ぶつぶつ言う

16. disband
1. 償う　　2. 解散する　　3. けんかする　　4. でっち上げる

17. rhyme
1. 遺品　　2. 排水路　　3. 特徴　　4. 韻

18. flick
1. 振り付ける　　2. 査定する　　3. 強化する　　4. 弾き飛ばす

19. pensive
1. 考え込んでいる　　2. 専売権のある　　3. 冬眠している　　4. 神にささげる

20. relativity
1. 相対性　　2. 器用さ　　3. 自由さ　　4. 信頼感

21. disperse
1. 楽しむ　　2. 散らかす　　3. 非難する　　4. 大声を出す

22. stint
1. おせっかい　　2. 馴れ合い　　3. 取り壊し　　4. 出し惜しみ

23. rueful
1. 様々な　　2. 哀れな　　3. 不道徳な　　4. 華やかな

24. stricture
1. 酷評　　2. 暴動　　3. 派閥　　4. 発想

25. ubiquitous
1. まねできない　　2. 至る所にある　　3. 意気消沈した　　4. とっぴな考えの

26. proscribe
1. 合致する　　2. 償却する　　3. 並列させる　　4. 禁止する

27. tactic
1. 戦術　　2. 召集　　3. 洞察力　　4. 皮肉

28. passbook
1. 攻略本　　2. 定期券　　3. パスポート　　4. 通帳

29. blanch
1. むしばむ　　2. 助長する　　3. 反発する　　4. 青ざめる

30. extraction
1. 拡張　　2. 成仏　　3. 抜歯　　4. 移植

31. rectitude
1. 熟練　　2. 正直　　3. 名声　　4. 覚書

32. quench
1. 具体化する　　2. 鎮める　　3. 魅了する　　4. 従う

33. tumultuous
1. 軽々しい　　2. 騒々しい　　3. 初々しい　　4. 荒々しい

34. leach
1. こし出す　　2. まとを得る　　3. 提携する　　4. 磨く

35. civility
1. 面倒　　2. 礼儀正しさ　　3. 不正　　4. 上品さ

36. 少数民族集団
1. enclave   2. backer   3. vanguard   4. pedigree

37. 崩壊
1. meteor   2. iniquity   3. forgery   4. disintegration

38. 静けさ
1. tranquility   2. epitome   3. precipitation   4. omen

39. 御影石
1. zealot   2. vantage   3. granite   4. promontory

40. 奨励
1. exhortation   2. rigor   3. coma   4. recitation

41. やわらぐ
1. quip   2. germinate   3. suffocate   4. relent

42. 就任させる
1. inaugurate   2. protrude   3. nag   4. grimace

1級
問題
②

43. 激怒
1. wrath   2. jubilee   3. naught   4. filth

44. 呼吸器官の
1. spinal   2. respiratory   3. digestive   4. maverick

45. 毛深い
1. shaggy   2. stark   3. flamboyant   4. porous

46. 骨董品
1. eviction   2. epitaph   3. curio   4. chisel

47. 口止めをする
1. gag   2. condone   3. ruffle   4. congregate

48. あざ笑う
1. woo   2. embroil   3. cull   4. scoff

49. 急にそれる
1. ratify   2. swerve   3. whine   4. jostle

50. せかす
1. gouge　　2. prod　　3. lathe　　4. stow

51. 再発する
1. relapse　　2. reminisce　　3. reverberate　　4. refurbish

52. 皮脂性の
1. creepy　　2. motley　　3. sebaceous　　4. rudimentary

53. 半透明の
1. transitory　　2. translucent　　3. pseudo　　4. ornate

54. 見かけ倒しの
1. shoddy　　2. copious　　3. genial　　4. infrared

55. ひどい
1. covert　　2. beastly　　3. touchy　　4. privy

56. 休止状態にある
1. moot　　2. staunch　　3. dormant　　4. defiant

57. おびき寄せる
1. scorch　　2. allure　　3. snarl　　4. tantalize

58. 捧げる
1. ransack　　2. consecrate　　3. scour　　4. spurt

59. 第一人者
1. exponent　　2. trooper　　3. entourage　　4. peddler

60. 宅配業者
1. savior　　2. suitor　　3. functionary　　4. courier

61. 歓喜
1. coercion　　2. mirth　　3. skeptic　　4. abstinence

62. 制止する
1. stipulate　　2. outstrip　　3. expedite　　4. deterrent

63. 封建主義
1. feudalism　　2. epicureanism　　3. polytheism　　4. barbarism

64. 芽を出す
1. fawn　　2. sprout　　3. huddle　　4. batten

65. 探知器
1. sedative　　2. insulation　　3. microbe　　4. detector

66. 美学
1. acoustics　　2. aesthetics　　3. entomology　　4. ethnology

67. 食い止める
1. stave　　2. impede　　3. vouch　　4. forge

68. 腹部の
1. abdominal　　2. colossal　　3. nuptial　　4. menial

69. 偽証
1. magnate　　2. zest　　3. perjury　　4. connoisseur

70. 耳を傾ける
1. appease　　2. hark　　3. usurp　　4. slither

③ 次の71. から85. までの説明文に最も適切な単語を、1,2,3,4の中から一つ
選びなさい。

71. very careful to be completely honest and fair
1. heinous　　2. scrupulous　　3. gracious　　4. demure

72. to hate something or someone very much
1. detest　　2. faint　　3. garnish　　4. snub

73. making you feel sad or full of pity
1. corpulent　　2. fluted　　3. poignant　　4. degraded

74. to treat somebody with too much care and attention
1. feign　　2. sully　　3. coddle　　4. bait

75. a person who supports a political party or set of ideas
1. reconciler　　2. protagonist　　3. pollster　　4. adherent

76. a very cruel, evil or violent person
1. benefactor　　2. fiend　　3. apprentice　　4. crone

77. the low continuous sound that a cat makes in its throat
1. ooze　　2. utter　　3. wobble　　4. purr

78. open and without shame about behaving in a wrong or immoral way
1. disdainful   2. agape   3. bewilder   4. brazen

79. to open a flag or sail
1. promulgate   2. incarnation   3. enthrall   4. unfurl

80. the reduction of something so that there is not enough left
1. depletion   2. disruption   3. frugality   4. insolvency

1級
問題
②

81. in an excited state and not able to think or speak clearly
1. delirious   2. flaccid   3. rampant   4. nefarious

82. willing to take risks or to do something shocking
1. cynical   2. audacious   3. exhume   4. ominous

83. slightly different in form or type from something else
1. omnipotent   2. impending   3. arbitrary   4. variant

84. a violent person, especially a criminal
1. barrister   2. canker   3. gnome   4. thug

85. a long wooden seat in a church
1. pew   2. vocation   3. ambience   4. plethora

④ 次の86. から100. までの単語に最も適切な説明文を、1,2,3,4の中から一
　つ選びなさい。

86. devious

1. intelligent, careful and showing good judgement, especially in business or politics
2. behaving in a dishonest or indirect way in order to get something
3. unpleasantly wet and cold
4. very determined to continue opposing someone or something

87. salvage

1. to save something from an accident or a bad situation
2. to make someone feel very shocked and upset
3. to become, and continue to be, successful, strong or healthy
4. to swell or make something swell, especially in an unpleasant way

88. kinetic

1. having an end or a limit
2. extremely large in number
3. of or produced by movement
4. in or moving through the air

89. larva

1. an insect at the stage when it has come out of an egg and looks like a short fat worm
2. any creature with a soft body that is divided into sections, and a hard outer shell
3. one of the foods that you use to make a particular food or dish
4. any of a group of natural substances which do not dissolve in water

90. spawn

1. to affect someone or something in an unpleasant way and make them suffer
2. to make a series of things happen or start to exist
3. to argue strongly in public for something you want especially a political
4. to take food or other substances into your body

91. perspiration

1. a ghost or an image of a person who is dead
2. a medical condition in which your skin and the white part of your eyes become yellow
3. immoral behavior involving drugs, alcohol or sex
4. drops of liquid that form on your skin when you are hot

92.　cumulative

1. increasing gradually as more of something is added or happens
2. expected to do something or to become something
3. being certain that your beliefs are right and that others should accept them
4. able to use the left hand or the right hand equally well

93.　debase

1. to make someone or something lose its value or people's respect
2. to prove that someone who was blamed for something is in fact not guilty
3. to do something in a different way from what is usual or expected
4. to refuse to give someone something

94.　wont

1. determined not to change your ideas, behavior or opinions
2. moving or tending to move away from a center
3. very delicate and light, in a way that does not seem real
4. in the habit of doing something

95.　grapple

1. to make somebody or something look or feel younger, more lively or more modern
2. to take a firm hold of somebody or something and struggle with them
3. to make something by using whatever you can find
4. to mix liquids or eggs into a stiff light mass, using a fork or special tool

96. epitomize

1. to make someone feel calmer when they have been angry
2. to be a very typical example of something
3. to do something that makes people lose respect for someone or something
4. to take off your hat, especially to show respect for somebody or something

97. vigilant

1. silly or amusing, especially when such behavior is not suitable
2. very careful to notice any signs of danger or trouble
3. talking a lot, especially about unimportant things
4. filled with horror and surprise when you see or hear something

98. wry

1. having no power to change things or to influence a situation
2. showing that you are both amused and disappointed or annoyed
3. designed to be useful and practical rather than attractive
4. having a meaning that is mysterious or not easily understood

99. commoner

1. a person who makes formal speeches in public or is good at public speaking
2. an old man who is respected as the head of a family or tribe
3. a person who does not come from a royal or noble family
4. a person in stories who uses magic and receives help from evil forces

100. scourge

1. something that causes a lot of harm or suffering
2. a sudden short period of angry, unreasonable behavior
3. a note in a piece of writing that explains a difficult word, phrase or idea
4. an atom which has been given a positive or negative force

解答

問1	問2	問3	問4	問5	問6	問7	問8	問9	問10
2	4	2	3	4	3	3	3	4	4
問11	問12	問13	問14	問15	問16	問17	問18	問19	問20
2	4	1	2	1	2	4	4	1	1
問21	問22	問23	問24	問25	問26	問27	問28	問29	問30
2	4	2	1	2	4	1	4	4	3
問31	問32	問33	問34	問35	問36	問37	問38	問39	問40
2	2	2	1	2	1	4	1	3	1
問41	問42	問43	問44	問45	問46	問47	問48	問49	問50
4	1	1	2	1	3	1	4	2	2
問51	問52	問53	問54	問55	問56	問57	問58	問59	問60
1	3	2	1	2	3	2	2	1	4
問61	問62	問63	問64	問65	問66	問67	問68	問69	問70
2	4	1	2	4	2	1	1	3	2
問71	問72	問73	問74	問75	問76	問77	問78	問79	問80
2	1	3	3	4	2	4	4	4	1
問81	問82	問83	問84	問85	問86	問87	問88	問89	問90
1	2	4	4	1	2	1	3	1	2
問91	問92	問93	問94	問95	問96	問97	問98	問99	問100
4	1	1	4	2	2	2	2	3	1

1級

問題③

① 次の1.から35.までの英単語の和訳として最も適切なものを1,2,3,4の中から一つ選びなさい。

1. zenith
1. 禁欲　　2. 絶頂　　3. 忠誠　　4. 天災

2. wean
1. 離婚する　　2. 離乳させる　　3. 死別する　　4. 決別させる

3. dormant
1. 愛している　　2. 治している　　3. 眠っている　　4. 蓄えている

4. squander
1. 浪費する　　2. 生還する　　3. 分割する　　4. 登場する

5. wrangle
1. 威嚇する　　2. 伝達する　　3. 口論する　　4. 拒絶する

6. precursor
1. ペテン師　　2. 先駆者　　3. 相場師　　4. 予言者

7. derision
1. 貴重な体験　　2. あざ笑い　　3. 無関心　　4. 自信喪失

8. wrath
1. 冒涜　2. 歓喜　3. 激怒　4. 悲観

9. lattice
1. 水周り　2. 壁材　3. 断熱材　4. 格子

10. locus
1. 場所　2. 公演　3. 神秘　4. 回転

11. sprig
1. 木の実　2. 発酵　3. 小枝　4. 発芽

12. molecular
1. 光線の　2. 分子の　3. 細胞の　4. 遺伝の

13. obliterate
1. 仮押さえする　2. 嚙み砕く　3. 消し去る　4. 染み込む

14. mortify
1. 悔しがらせる　2. 押しつける　3. 黙らせる　4. 知らしめる

15. flirtation
1. めいわくなこと　　2. しつこいこと　　3. こだわること　　4. いちゃつくこと

16. mold
1. 練金　　2. 型　　3. 溶接　　4. 研磨

17. hideous
1. みじめな　　2. 立ち直れない　　3. ぞっとする　　4. 極秘の

18. bladder
1. ふくらんだもの　　2. 丸いもの　　3. 危険なもの　　4. 鋭いもの

19. exhort
1. 頻繁に通う　　2. 過呼吸になる　　3. 強く勧める　　4. 情熱的になる

20. exposition
1. 支援金　　2. 外商員　　3. 展示会　　4. 昇格試験

21. warren
1. 危険な場所　　2. 狭い場所　　3. 静かな場所　　4. ごみごみした場所

22. fickle
1. 華奢な　　2. 雑な　　3. 気まぐれな　　4. 怪しげな

23. usurp
1. 奪う　　2. 尋ねる　　3. 鍛える　　4. 戦う

24. alight
1. 告発する　　2. 降りる　　3. 触れる　　4. 電源を入れる

25. brutality
1. 万能　　2. 野蛮　　3. 熱愛　　4. 溺愛

26. revoke
1. 故障する　　2. 廃止する　　3. 再選する　　4. 導入する

27. prod
1. 勧告する　　2. 刺激する　　3. 棄権する　　4. 応援する

28. frock
1. 私服　　2. 部屋着　　3. 礼服　　4. 仕事着

29. hyperbole
1. 誇張　　2. 躊躇　　3. 名声　　4. 秘伝

30. oust
1. 追い出す　　2. 冷ます　　3. 分け与える　　4. 巻く

31. harry
1. ゆっくり伸ばす　　2. 静かに過ごす　　3. うるさく求める　　4. しっかり断る

32. embellish
1. 横領する　　2. 加熱する　　3. 強制する　　4. 装飾する

33. sacrilegious
1. 被害の　　2. 儀式の　　3. 神聖の　　4. 罰当たりの

34. illicit
1. 不慮の　　2. 不正な　　3. 不滅の　　4. 不慣れな

35. acumen
1. まぶしい光　　2. 高い運動神経　　3. 鋭い洞察力　　4. 低い成長性

36. 例外
1. canopy　　2. caucus　　3. anomaly　　4. exemplar

37. 教区牧師
1. quip　　2. parson　　3. kindred　　4. covenant

38. お祭りの
1. curt　　2. trite　　3. coy　　4. gala

39. 引き出す
1. elicit　　2. pacify　　3. constrain　　4. emanate

40. 周囲
1. periphery　　2. presage　　3. squint　　4. pedigree

41. 即席の
1. intravenous　　2. stupendous　　3. preposterous　　4. extemporaneous

42. 撲滅する
1. vanquish　　2. eradicate　　3. concoct　　4. dissect

43.　典型
1. panacea　　2. epitome　　3. imposition　　4. adhesive

44.　送金
1. courier　　2. pelvis　　3. flux　　4. remittance

45.　罰金
1. impetus　　2. forfeit　　3. volition　　4. diarrhea

46.　崇拝
1. oracle　　2. adoration　　3. crucifixion　　4. psalm

47.　分枝
1. czar　　2. conflagration　　3. ramification　　4. clairvoyant

48.　明るくて優しい
1. subversive　　2. lamentable　　3. genial　　4. giddy

49.　大胆不敵な
1. dingy　　2. intrepid　　3. porous　　4. blatant

50. すす
1. laurel   2. wedge   3. soot   4. stag

51. 病原菌
1. microbe   2. balk   3. hepatitis   4. antidote

52. 叱責
1. reprimand   2. pun   3. coronation   4. trimming

53. 小滝
1. predator   2. inlet   3. cascade   4. skull

54. 親善
1. innuendo   2. treachery   3. ingratitude   4. amity

1級
問題
③

55. 分離
1. schism   2. visage   3. flank   4. epicenter

56. がれき
1. fluff   2. heather   3. rubble   4. harrow

57. 議論の
1. audible   2. malign   3. glib   4. polemic

58. 大荒れ
1. sortie   2. tenure   3. havoc   4. clout

59. 嫌って
1. averse   2. obese   3. elusive   4. sparse

60. 持ち上げる
1. quell   2. heave   3. sulk   4. nestle

61. 偽物
1. truce   2. admonition   3. stench   4. sham

62. ひるむ
1. eject   2. flinch   3. suffocate   4. insinuate

63. とげのある
1. disheveled   2. unauthorized   3. barbed   4. dilapidated

64. 名簿
1. rodent   2. roster   3. nomad   4. cordon

65. 見せかけの
1. indelible   2. feasible   3. ostensible   4. invincible

66. しみ出る
1. pamper   2. exude   3. wield   4. wheeze

67. 詩人
1. muck   2. fodder   3. picket   4. bard

68. 病的な
1. idiosyncratic   2. antiseptic   3. morbid   4. sardonic

69. 武勇伝
1. prodigy   2. pall   3. hermit   4. saga

70. 元気づける
1. gild   2. mitigate   3. baffle   4. perk

③ 次の71. から85. までの説明文に最も適切な単語を、1,2,3,4の中から一つ
   選びなさい。

71. badly made and not strong enough for the purpose for which it is used
1. derelict　　2. urbane　　3. somber　　4. flimsy

72. peaceful and beautiful or perfect without problems
1. idyllic　　2. sanguine　　3. haughty　　4. sumptuous

73. completely ready to do something or for something to happen
1. retarded　　2. poised　　3. disadvantaged　　4. dogged

74. to give a particular quality to something
1. brandish　　2. divergent　　3. impart　　4. gloat

75. to attack someone by throwing a lot of things at them
1. muffle　　2. curtail　　3. constrict　　4. pelt

76. the natural color and condition of the skin on a person's face
1. whim　　2. forte　　3. smudge　　4. complexion

77. the moral ideas and attitudes that belong to a particular group or society

1. niche   2. orgy   3. embryo   4. ethos

78. to combine two or more things together to make one thing

1. jeopardize   2. amalgamate   3. dilate   4. deduce

79. showing that you think you are more important than other people

1. valiant   2. pompous   3. futility   4. circumspect

80. the first public performance of a film or music

1. defiance   2. turnout   3. lineage   4. premiere

81. sounding rough and unpleasant because of a sore throat

1. impudent   2. jovial   3. morose   4. hoarse

82. so interested in one particular thing that you are not notice anything else

1. cardinal   2. brittle   3. rapt   4. abject

83. to prove that a statement or an idea is not correct

1. consummate   2. assail   3. refute   4. jeopardize

1級
問題
③

84. a small sign of something

1. glimmer   2. vagabond   3. naught   4. bravado

85. a person who represents a particular quality in human form

1. incarnation   2. secession   3. combustion   4. contraception

④ 次の86. から100. までの単語に最も適切な説明文を、1,2,3,4の中から一
つ選びなさい。

86. quay

1. a place in a town or village where boats can be tied up or can stop to load
   goods
2. a small open boat used for pleasure or for taking people between a ship and
   the shore
3. a small narrow valley formed by a lot of rain flowing down the side of a hill
4. a small hill of sand formed by the wind near the sea or in a desert

87. agile

1. good or quick at noticing things
2. intended to cause very strong feelings of anger
3. able to think quickly and in an intelligent way
4. believing strongly in a particular religion

1級
問題
③

88. denunciation

1. a well-known phrase expressing a general truth about people or the world
2. a place in a river or the sea where currents of water spin round very fast
3. a public statement in which you criticize someone or something
4. a belief that you have been treated unfairly

89. squat

1. to persuade somebody to do something by talking to them in a kind and gentle way
2. to persuade somebody to give you something or do something by saying nice things
3. to sit on your heels with your knees bent up close to your body
4. to get back something that you have lost or that has been taken away from you

90. outlay

1. an agreement in which you win or lose money according to the result of something
2. a document that shows how much you owe somebody for goods or services
3. the money that you have to spend in order to start a new project
4. a small flat piece of metal used as money

91. upstart

1. someone who has more than a billion dollars or pounds
2. someone who is the first to study and develop a particular area of knowledge
3. someone who has a natural ability to do something well
4. someone who behaves as if they were more important than they really are

92. mutation
1. an enjoyable and amusing occasion or thing that happens
2. a fault in something or in the way it has been made which means that it is not perfect
3. a change in the genetic structure of an animal or plant
4. a spiritual change when a person's faith becomes stronger

93. apparition
1. a state similar to sleep in which someone's actions can be influenced by someone else
2. a special quality or ability that somebody or something has
3. a ghost or an image of a person who is dead
4. a way of doing something that works very well but may not be easy to notice

94. moribund
1. moving in a way that is not smooth or elegant
2. relating to the treatment or cure of an illness
3. rude and not showing respect for somebody who is older or more important
4. no longer effective and about to come to an end completely

1級
問題
③

95.　abreast

1. next to somebody or something and facing the same way
2. a feeling that is tepid shows a lack of excitement or interest
3. planned or done so carefully that there is no chance of any problems or mistakes
4. very delicate and light in a way that does not seem real

96.　evict

1. to cheat somebody in order to get something from them
2. to decide and state officially in court that somebody is not guilty of a crime
3. to force somebody to leave a house or land when you have the legal right to do so
4. to give an example in order to make something clearer

97.　fret

1. to speak or say something slowly with vowel sounds that are longer than usual
2. to criticize somebody or something in a way that shows how much you dislike them
3. to be worried or unhappy and not able to relax
4. to decide not to have or do something that you would like to have or do

98. accolade

1. work that you do or something that you have made
2. the process of saving money for a special purpose
3. a chemical substance that is produced in a plant or animal
4. praise or an award for an achievement that people admire

99. motley

1. having a very harmful effect on something in a way that is gradual
2. sharing in the knowledge of facts that are secret
3. consisting of many different types of things that do not seem to belong together
4. behaving too confidently and speaking too loudly

100. resurrect

1. to change what you are doing so that you are not following an expected plan or idea
2. to be repeated several times as it is reflected off different surfaces
3. to close a business or company and sell the things that belong to it
4. to bring back an old activity, a belief or an idea that hadn't existed for a long time

1級
問題
③

解答

問1	問2	問3	問4	問5	問6	問7	問8	問9	問10
2	2	3	1	3	2	2	3	4	1

問11	問12	問13	問14	問15	問16	問17	問18	問19	問20
3	2	3	1	4	2	3	1	3	3

問21	問22	問23	問24	問25	問26	問27	問28	問29	問30
4	3	1	2	2	2	2	4	1	1

問31	問32	問33	問34	問35	問36	問37	問38	問39	問40
3	4	4	2	3	3	2	4	1	1

問41	問42	問43	問44	問45	問46	問47	問48	問49	問50
4	2	2	4	2	2	3	3	2	3

問51	問52	問53	問54	問55	問56	問57	問58	問59	問60
1	1	3	4	1	3	4	3	1	2

問61	問62	問63	問64	問65	問66	問67	問68	問69	問70
4	2	3	2	3	2	4	3	4	4

問71	問72	問73	問74	問75	問76	問77	問78	問79	問80
4	1	2	3	4	4	4	2	2	4

問81	問82	問83	問84	問85	問86	問87	問88	問89	問90
4	3	3	1	1	1	3	3	3	3

問91	問92	問93	問94	問95	問96	問97	問98	問99	問100
4	3	3	4	1	3	3	4	3	4

1級

問題④

① 次の1. から35. までの英単語の和訳として最も適切なものを1,2,3,4の中から一つ選びなさい。

1.　clientele
1. 新規客　　2. 見込客　　3. 顧客達　　4. クレーマー

2.　enshrine
1. 完済する　　2. 安置する　　3. 注入する　　4. 任命する

3.　clout
1. 遠心力　　2. 爆発力　　3. 信用力　　4. 影響力

4.　grimace
1. 強い憎しみ　　2. しかめ面　　3. 慌てぶり　　4. 平静

5.　sludge
1. 黒鉛　　2. わだち　　3. ゴミ溜め　　4. ぬかるみ

6.　trough
1. 支え板　　2. やすり　　3. くぼみ　　4. 棺桶

7.　circumscribe
1. 書面にする　　2. 環境保全する　　3. 制限する　　4. 丸を書く

8. arbitration
1. 褒章　　2. 乱立　　3. 比較　　4. 仲裁

9. pounce
1. 急に襲う　　2. 急に倒れる　　3. 急に滑る　　4. 急に思いつく

10. rebuff
1. 報酬　　2. 拒絶　　3. 返還　　4. 反感

11. contemplative
1. 封建的な　　2. 改革的な　　3. 情緒的な　　4. 静観的な

12. ulcer
1. 傍聴　　2. 遠戚　　3. 弊害　　4. 狂信

13. forgery
1. 温情　　2. 利権　　3. 偽造　　4. 戦力

14. membrane
1. 薄膜　　2. 表情筋　　3. 食道　　4. 分泌物

15. lair
1. 隠れ家　　2. 敵陣　　3. 野獣　　4. 先頭

16. postulate
1. 委託する　　2. 売却する　　3. 仮定する　　4. 投函する

17. whirlwind
1. 横風　　2. 全力　　3. 忙殺　　4. 新風

18. ante
1. 相続金　　2. 賭け金　　3. 損金　　4. 保険金

19. glum
1. ほっとした　　2. いらいらした　　3. むっつりした　　4. わくわくした

20. projectile
1. 教養を身につける　　2. 有名になる　　3. 計画する　　4. 発射する

21. altruism
1. 独立主義　　2. 平和主義　　3. 資本主義　　4. 利他主義

22. pilfer
1. 助け合う　　2. 投げやりになる　　3. 注意深く見る　　4. 盗む

23. itinerary
1. 特例処置　　2. 旅行日程　　3. 定期診断　　4. 親善行事

24. prolific
1. 高貴の　　2. 先天性の　　3. 多産の　　4. 専門の

25. kindred
1. 侵略　　2. 他薦　　3. 血縁　　4. 親切

26. crucifixion
1. 作り話　　2. 虚構　　3. 苦しい試練　　4. 板ばさみ

27. inertia
1. 停刊　　2. 妙技　　3. 慣性　　4. 崩落

28. warden
1. 管理人　　2. 寮生　　3. まかない　　4. 共同生活

29. matron
1. 寮母　2. 超大作　3. 高級品　4. 主権

30. asteroid
1. 陥落　2. 小惑星　3. 鎮静剤　4. 海底世界

31. ointment
1. 両天秤　2. 独りよがり　3. 接待　4. 軟膏

32. havoc
1. 破壊　2. 緊張　3. 愛情　4. 勝因

33. affiliate
1. 加入させる　2. 横流しする　3. 儲けされる　4. 補助する

34. resurrect
1. 再選する　2. 復興する　3. 採択する　4. 喚起する

35. influx
1. 発表　2. 殺到　3. 収入　4. 設置

次の36. から70. までの日本語の英訳として最も適切なものを、1,2,3,4の中から一つ選びなさい。

36.　気持よく横たわる
1. muddle　　2. allay　　3. nestle　　4. counteract

37.　非常に用心深く
1. stuffy　　2. gingerly　　3. auxiliary　　4. ancillary

38.　一点に集まる
1. wrangle　　2. hurtle　　3. galvanize　　4. converge

39.　にやにや笑う
1. smirk　　2. insinuate　　3. augment　　4. evict

40.　分析する
1. totter　　2. annex　　3. detract　　4. assay

41.　はっきりさせる
1. pout　　2. fret　　3. elucidate　　4. devolve

1級
問題
④

42.　一定配給量
1. jut　　2. ration　　3. larva　　4. clamp

43. 意気揚々とした
1. touchy   2. perky   3. stingy   4. predatory

44. 隔離する
1. quench   2. condone   3. deflect   4. insulate

45. 信徒席
1. asylum   2. pew   3. torso   4. rostrum

46. 罪滅ぼしをする
1. jostle   2. atone   3. deplore   4. secede

47. 差し出す
1. impel   2. tangle   3. proffer   4. refute

48. 発泡性の
1. facile   2. ubiquitous   3. effervescent   4. benevolent

49. 気まぐれ
1. resin   2. maggot   3. pseudonym   4. prognosis

50. 集合する
1. deride　　2. oscillate　　3. aggregate　　4. delude

51. 手詰まり
1. stalemate　　2. clamor　　3. acclamation　　4. cataclysm

52. 完全に破壊する
1. raze　　2. vindicate　　3. slur　　4. topple

53. 小峡谷
1. muck　　2. sperm　　3. gully　　4. crease

54. 便秘
1. adoration　　2. asthma　　3. constipation　　4. corollary

55. 聴く
1. pacify　　2. flit　　3. stipulate　　4. hark

56. チョキンと切る
1. allure　　2. transcend　　3. snip　　4. batten

1級
問題
④

57. うつむいた
1. squalid   2. morbid   3. irredeemable   4. downcast

58. 倒壊させる
1. daunt   2. subversive   3. dangle   4. construe

59. 独裁の
1. bureaucratic   2. geometric   3. prosaic   4. autocratic

60. 邪魔する
1. thwart   2. antagonize   3. abate   4. brewery

61. 切断する
1. sag   2. purr   3. mutilate   4. seep

62. 移り気の
1. fickle   2. brash   3. vindictive   4. seedy

63. 水門
1. lava   2. sluice   3. bison   4. moratorium

64. 改ざんする
1. refurbish   2. tamper   3. ransack   4. resuscitate

65. 口の達者な
1. sedate   2. bashful   3. glib   4. taut

66. 適切な
1. culinary   2. pertinent   3. exuberant   4. imperative

67. がれき
1. nook   2. memento   3. beacon   4. rubble

68. 強い憎しみ
1. solidarity   2. animosity   3. amnesty   4. sanctity

69. さい先のよい
1. omnivorous   2. indigenous   3. auspicious   4. ponderous

70. おびき寄せる
1. alight   2. usurp   3. scorch   4. decoy

③ 次の71. から85. までの説明文に最も適切な単語を、1,2,3,4の中から一つ
　選びなさい。

71. a place in a river or the sea where currents of water spin round very fast
1. brawl　　2. vane　　3. whirlpool　　4. vale

72. the act of asking somebody a lot of questions over a long period of time
1. precedence　　2. deterrence　　3. conglomerate　　4. interrogation

73. burning strongly with a lot of flames
1. trident　　2. ablaze　　3. astute　　4. strident

74. to delay something until a later date
1. sear　　2. modulate　　3. defer　　4. seclude

75. the quality of thinking or behaving in a correct and honest way
1. tome　　2. dictum　　3. rectitude　　4. makeshift

76. a confident way of behaving that is intended to impress people
1. zodiac　　2. placebo　　3. bravado　　4. stag

77. to think that something is likely to happen in the future
1. sever   2. unfurl   3. glimmer   4. envisage

78. action against someone who has done something bad to you
1. aberration   2. retaliation   3. ammunition   4. bastion

79. secret and mysterious and therefore difficult to understand
1. resplendent   2. arcane   3. schematic   4. fraught

80. someone who is eligible for something is able or allowed to do it
1. hem   2. fissure   3. exemplar   4. eligible

81. happy talk, enjoyment and the sound of people laughing
1. pigment   2. rapprochement   3. impediment   4. merriment

82. the quality of being famous and respected especially in a profession
1. complicity   2. dredge   3. eminence   4. allegiance

1級
問題
④

83. seeming to be the reason for or the purpose of something
1. ludicrous   2. gallant   3. ostensible   4. statutory

84. easily annoyed by small and unimportant things

1. peevish   2. expedient   3. lenient   4. caustic

85. to gradually stop feeding a baby or young animal with its mother's milk

1. wean   2. elicit   3. bode   4. cower

④ 次の86. から100. までの単語に最も適切な説明文を、1,2,3,4の中から一
   つ選びなさい。

86. retard

1. to ask somebody for something in a very strong and serious way
2. to make somebody very interested and want to know more about
   something
3. to persuade or influence somebody to do something
4. to make something happen more slowly than expected

87. concordance

1. a device that controls the amount of fuel that goes into the engine of a
   vehicle
2. an order or a rule made by a government or somebody in a position of
   authority
3. an alphabetical list of all the words used in a book or set of books
4. a story in which each character or event is a symbol representing an idea or
   a quality

88. fugitive

1. a person who has done something wrong or against the law
2. a person who has escaped or is running away from somewhere
3. a person or thing that takes the place of someone or something else
4. a person that you feel sympathy or pity for

89. ecclesiastical

1. thinking carefully about something before doing it, in order to avoid risk
2. relating to the Christian Church or its clergy
3. being something in name only and not in reality
4. relating to positions, jobs or relationships that are at the same level or rank

90. fussy

1. not willing to give clear answers to a question
2. doing something with small, quick and nervous movements
3. having two halves, parts or sides that are the same in size and shape
4. looking or feeling embarrassed because you have done something silly or wrong

91. squatter

1. a person who makes formal speeches in public or is good at public speaking
2. a person who is living in a building or on land without permission and without paying rent
3. a person who gives secret information about somebody or something to the police
4. a person who is sent with an official message or to do official work

92. abyss

1. a very deep wide space or hole that seems to have no bottom
2. a strong base for the facts or the principles on which it is based
3. a strong feeling of dislike or fear of people from other countries
4. a ghost or an image of a person who is dead

93. secession
1. the sudden appearance of something in a particular area of activity
2. the fact of an area or group becoming independent from the country
3. the destruction and end of the world
4. the painting's delicate nuances of color, tone and texture

94. peruse
1. to succeed in dealing with a problem or difficulty
2. to read something, especially in a careful way
3. to make people feel something more strongly
4. to perform a play or act a part in a play

95. clockwise
1. happening or doing something at the arranged or correct time
2. suitable and right for a particular situation
3. quick at learning and understanding things
4. moving around in the same direction as the hands of a clock

96. inception
1. a device that gives extra power to a piece of electrical equipment
2. the start of an institution or an organization
3. a way of explaining something to make it seem more attractive or acceptable
4. a feeling of pain that you experience as a series of strong

1級
問題
④

97. intoxicate

1. to make somebody or something look or feel younger, more lively or more modern
2. to cause somebody to lose control of their behavior or their physical and mental abilities
3. to limit something or make it last for a shorter time
4. to find or choose information from many different places

98. appease

1. to have too high an opinion of somebody or something
2. to put or pack something tidily away in a space until you need it again
3. to make somebody calmer or less angry by giving them what they want
4. to give someone the political or legal rights that they did not have before

99. impasse

1. an agreement between enemies or opponents to stop fighting for an agreed period of time
2. a difficult situation in which no progress can be made
3. a rule on which a way of thinking or behaving is based
4. an excuse for something you have failed to do or have done wrong

100. circumspect

1. behaving in an unfair or dishonest way
2. thinking very carefully about something before doing it in order to avoid risks
3. having two of something or two parts
4. involving a lot of change and confusion or violence

解答

問 1	問 2	問 3	問 4	問 5	問 6	問 7	問 8	問 9	問 10
3	2	4	2	4	3	3	4	1	2

問 11	問 12	問 13	問 14	問 15	問 16	問 17	問 18	問 19	問 20
4	3	3	1	1	3	3	2	3	4

問 21	問 22	問 23	問 24	問 25	問 26	問 27	問 28	問 29	問 30
4	4	2	3	3	3	3	1	1	2

問 31	問 32	問 33	問 34	問 35	問 36	問 37	問 38	問 39	問 40
4	1	1	2	2	3	2	4	1	4

問 41	問 42	問 43	問 44	問 45	問 46	問 47	問 48	問 49	問 50
3	2	2	4	2	2	3	3	2	3

問 51	問 52	問 53	問 54	問 55	問 56	問 57	問 58	問 59	問 60
1	1	3	3	4	3	4	2	4	1

問 61	問 62	問 63	問 64	問 65	問 66	問 67	問 68	問 69	問 70
3	1	2	2	3	2	4	2	3	4

問 71	問 72	問 73	問 74	問 75	問 76	問 77	問 78	問 79	問 80
3	4	2	3	3	3	4	2	2	4

問 81	問 82	問 83	問 84	問 85	問 86	問 87	問 88	問 89	問 90
4	3	3	1	1	4	3	2	2	2

問 91	問 92	問 93	問 94	問 95	問 96	問 97	問 98	問 99	問 100
2	1	2	2	4	2	2	3	2	2

日本英会話協会について

　(財)日本英会話協会は、2009年に日本人の英会話力向上を目指し、世界で活躍する人材
を育成するために設立されました。◎講演活動 ◎資格検定 ◎英会話に関する情報発信
等で教育をサポートし、アジアで最下位と言われている日本人の英語力を上げ、世界で
活躍できる人材と企業の育成に力を入れております。

英単語検定とは？

　(財)日本英会話協会による英単語の知識に特化した資格検定試験です。中学低学年レベル
の５級からネイティブレベルの１級まで７つのレベルがあり、ご自分の「語彙力」をテス
トすることができます。全級共通して試験問題は100問あり、級があがるにつれて問題の
内容がより高度になっていきます。TOEICや英検のような複雑な文法、長文読解問題は
ありません。英語の長文読解に関して言えば、英単語が分かれば全体の70%は理解できる
といわれています。単語の意味を理解することで周辺の文脈が自然に類推できるからで
しょう。英語・英会話学習にとって最も重要である「語彙力」をチェックし、あなたの
英語力にさらに磨きをかけて下さい。

ホームページ

　http://www.eitangokentei.com/

英単語検定 [単検] 公式問題集　1級

2017年2月13日　　初 版 発 行
2021年2月16日　　第二刷発行

　　　　　　　　　一般財団法人日本英会話協会　　監修

発行所　　株 式 会 社　　三 恵 社
〒462-0056 愛知県名古屋市北区中丸町2-24-1
TEL 052 (915) 5211
FAX 052 (915) 5019
URL http://www.sankeisha.com

乱丁・落丁の場合はお取替えいたします。

ISBN978-4-86487-595-0 C0082